Longmans' Pocket Library

F. ANSTEY.
Voces Populi. Two Series. With Illustrations by J. BERNARD PARTRIDGE.

SIR EDWIN ARNOLD.
The Light of the World; or, The Great Consummation. With Photogravure Frontispiece after HOLMAN HUNT.

W. DE LA MARE.
Songs of Childhood.

J. A. FROUDE.
Short Studies on Great Subjects. 5 volumes.

H. R. GAMBLE.
Christianity and Common Life: Sermons.

JEAN INGELOW.
Poems. Selected and Arranged by ANDREW LANG.

RICHARD JEFFERIES.
The Story of My Heart.

ANDREW LANG.
New and Old Letters to Dead Authors.

Ballads and Lyrics of Old France.

Ballades and Rhymes.

Books and Bookmen.

Old Friends.

CANON LIDDON.
Sermons at St. Paul's and Elsewhere.

J. W. MACKAIL.
Select Epigrams from the Greek Anthology. 2 vols. Greek Text—English Translation.

The Eclogues and Georgics of Virgil. Translated into English Prose.

Sayings of Christ. Collected and Arranged from the Gospels.

F. MAX MÜLLER.
Deutsche Liebe (German Love). With Portrait.

WILLIAM MORRIS.
The Life of William Morris. By J. W. MACKAIL. 2 vo's. With Frontispieces.

The Life and Death of Jason. A Poem.

Poems by the Way.

News from Nowhere. (In Paper Covers, 1s. net.)

A Dream of John Ball and A King's Lesson.

The House of the Wolfings.

The Roots of the Mountains. 2 vols.

The Story of the Glittering Plain.

The Wood Beyond the World.

The Well at the World's End. 2 vols.

The Water of the Wondrous Isles. 2 vols.

The Sundering Flood. 2 vols.

The Pilgrims of Hope and Chants for Socialists.

The Defence of Guenevere, and Other Poems.

CANON NEWBOLT.
The Gospel Message.

CARDINAL NEWMAN.
Verses on Various Occasions (including "The Dream of Gerontius").

The Church of the Fathers.

University Teaching.

Apologia Pro Vitâ Suâ. (Cloth, 2/6 net; Leather, 4/- net.)

R. L. STEVENSON.
Dr. Jekyll and Mr. Hyde, with other Fables.

A Child's Garden of Verses.

More New Arabian Nights— The Dynamiter.

The Wrong Box.

STANLEY WEYMAN.
The House of the Wolf.

LONGMANS, GREEN AND CO.
LONDON, NEW YORK, BOMBAY, CALCUTTA, AND MADRAS

A CHILD'S GARDEN

OF VERSES

Alison Cunningham.

A CHILD'S GARDEN

OF VERSES

BY

ROBERT LOUIS STEVENSON

WITH AN INTRODUCTION BY ANDREW LANG

AND A FRONTISPIECE

Pocket Edition

NEW IMPRESSION

LONGMANS, GREEN AND CO.
39 PATERNOSTER ROW, LONDON
FOURTH AVENUE & 30TH STREET, NEW YORK
BOMBAY, CALCUTTA, AND MADRAS
1916

BIBLIOGRAPHICAL NOTE.

Original Edition,
First printed March 1885.

*Reprinted July 1885, May 1888, August 1890,
January 1893, December 1894, January 1895,
January 1897, March 1899, January 1902,
March 1904, March 1906.*

Illustrated Edition (LONGMANS, GREEN, & Co.)
October 1905.

*Pocket Edition, March 1907. New Impression
June 1907, November 1907, August 1908, October
1909, January 1911, October 1912, January 1914,
and November 1916.*

TO ALISON CUNNINGHAM

FROM HER BOY

*F*OR *the long nights you lay awake*
    And watched for my unworthy sake:
For your most comfortable hand
That led me through the uneven land:
For all the story-books you read:
For all the pains you comforted:
For all you pitied, all you bore,
In sad and happy days of yore:—
My second Mother, my first Wife,
The angel of my infant life—
From the sick child, now well and old,
Take, nurse, the little book you hold!

And grant it, Heaven, that all who read
May find as dear a nurse at need,
And every child who lists my rhyme,
In the bright, fireside, nursery clime,
May hear it in as kind a voice
As made my childish days rejoice!

                                     R. L.

INTRODUCTION

THIS little volume leads the memory back, far
across 'the gulf whose waves are year by year.'
In 1885, when 'A Child's Garden of Verses'
was published, the author was still, I think,
the youngest of a little group of friends who
were fond of books and of lunching together
at a certain club. It was yet more pleasant,
though wickedly selfish, to induce Mr. Stevenson to lunch at another club, where you had
him all to yourself. In those days he had for
ten years at least been the bright particular
star of the group : there was no one like him,
whether as essayist, or as author of the rarely
fantastic 'New Arabian Nights,' that *mélange*
of stately banter, horror, burlesque, and vivid

invention. He had shown, too, his power as a narrator by his romance for boys, 'Treasure Island,' so cunning in style, so fertile in fancy, so masterly in the creation of Silver, that crutched buccaneer, and of the terrible blind Pew whose staff tapped with a terrifying sound, as (to quote the author of his being) 'He beckled, beckled all the way.' Finally Mr. Stevenson had won a path into the good graces of pulpit orators by the gruesome moral allegory of 'The Strange Case of Dr. Jekyll and Mr. Hyde.'

The moral allegory I never could applaud: Mr. Hyde was not a good man, not one whom you could propose as a member of any club, with hope of his success, but Dr. Jekyll also was not a good man, and was less like a gentleman than his co-walker.

The peculiarity of Mr. Stevenson, among the set with whom he lived most when in London, was that he had never published verses. Most of the others had begun by attempting the strait and narrow way of verse, however obscurely, and however contemptuous, by 1885, may have been their own opinion of what Keats calls their 'early blights.'

Mr. Stevenson, so far as his path was open to the sun and the eye of observers, had never even signed a copy of verses in a magazine. Then, unexpectedly, he blossomed on a new bough, and gave us 'A Child's Garden of Verses.' 'Shall I confess it or shall I conceal it?' as people say in Homer. The secret is that I could never read the book without 'a great inclinations to cry.' The poems bring back so vividly, to some students, 'Another child, far, far away'—another child, absorbed in story books, lost in Shakespeare or Scott, perhaps seated under the table while the elders talk beside the fire or someone sings. Not all of us have been bookish children, but we who were bookish acted the scenes of which they read, and I remember, as a Roman engineer, taking part in the siege of Jerusalem, with a battering ram which, to the eyes of adults, bore the aspect of a long hard round cushion. The least bookish child, or grown-up who was once a child, and remembers the

emotions of that age, recognises the sentiment
in

> And does it not seem hard to you,
> When all the sky is clear and blue,
> And I should like so much to play,
> To have to go to bed by day?

To have to go to bed when the hills beyond
Ettrick were purple against the silver light of
a summer evening had but one compensating
advantage.   There were no shadowy passages
to tread on the darksome way, and there was
no fear, as in winter darkness, of seeing a
spectre who, as spectres will, brought his own
light with him.

The Stèvenson child, he has told us, was
the victim of nocturnal fears which seem to
have been the baseless and unhistoric creation
of his own powerful fancy.   That other child,
of whom I am reminiscent, had no more
imagination than an oyster, but was cursed
with an encyclopædic literary knowledge of
every species of spook, from the *glastic* (I hope
the orthography is correct), to the worst of

the species, a Vampire. Wraiths, Banshees,
the relatively harmless Brownie, the odious
phantasm of the human dead who comes back
as a shapeless animal, and ' the spectral hound
of Man :' with Michael Scott, who was a neigh-
bour, and might appear at home as easily as
in Branksome Hall—more easily, the distance
from his grave was shorter,—this child knew
them, and expected their visits. The Stevenson
child does not seem to have been so much of a
specialist in spectres. He says :

Now my little heart goes a-beating like a drum,
With the breath of the Bogie in my hair.

' Bogie ' is vague, is undifferentiated. The
child Stevenson was a born wanderer :

If I could find a higher tree
Farther and farther I should see,
To where the grown-up river slips
Into the sea among the ships.

The grown-up Stevenson still, in the windy
darkness, heard

Late in the night when the fires are out,
  A man go riding by.

This is the man who rattled with his whip handle, as he passed, on the shutters of the little inn at Burford Bridge, in one of the many romances that Mr. Stevenson dreamed of, but never wrote.

Like most, perhaps all, men of genius, he was always a child, and always a boy. He loved a boat like that other eternal boy, Shelley.

Should a leaflet come to land,
Drifting near to where I stand,
Straight I'll board that little boat,
Round the rain-pool sea to float.

Shelley, too, has the leaf-boat somewhere, but Mr. Stevenson did not borrow it from him. Again, in 'A Child's Garden,' we find :

Green leaves a-floating,
  Castles of the foam,
Boats of mine a-boating—
  Where will all come home ?

He turns all into romance ; who that was a child in the country does not remember the fragrant hills, the delectable mountains of the shadowy hayloft ?

> Here is Mount Clear, Mount Rusty-Nail,
>   Mount Eagle and Mount High ;
> The mice that in these mountains dwell,
>   No happier are than I !

> ('The Gods that wanton in the air
>   Know no such liberty.')

No doubt the voice of the man imitates the childish treble, and he can't but be conscious of the pathos, but only a man with the child awake in him could write of his chief treasure,

> A chisel, both handle and blade,
> Which a man who was really a carpenter
>   made.

> All his life he was 'playing at things,' as of
>   when

a

With my little gun I crawl
All in the dark along the wall,
And follow round the forest track
Away behind the sofa back.

I have never known, I have never asked,
how much he played at being the conspirator
in Samoa, and how openly he wore the White
Cockade for the Samoan royal exile, the king
over the water, Malietoa Mataafa. Malietoa
Mataafa, a name to fight and die for, so it
sounds, but at the time it was best, as the man
in 'Jekyll and Hyde' says, to ask no questions,
and now, who could answer them?

'The Gardener' reappears, I fancy, in one
of Mr. Stevenson's essays.

'Silly gardener!' he cries, for the gardener
does not love to talk.

Far in the plots, I see him dig,
Old and serious, brown and big.

Scottish gardeners less silly the other child
has known. Who dug the worms for bait?
Who put them on the hook? Who showed you
how to drop them into the little white linn,

and let them float into the black pool where the
trout lay waiting? Who made the bows and
arrows? Who re-strung the bats? Who,
when a game was being organised, always
asked, 'What side am I on?'—THE GARDENER.

We find, as the poems tell us, that the Stevenson child 'played at things,' but not at games
where the captains toss up and choose sides.
He was too dramatic, too much of a poet.
Had he lived in town you would not have seen
him batting with a tree for a wicket, and
sisters bowling to him balls that always go
as far astray as Mr. Bosanquet's deliveries
occasionally do. In the Serpentine and the
Round Pond, and the Alleys of Trees, he would
have seen

> The silver river, the sounding sea,
> And the robber woods of Tartary.

It never was true of him that

> The eternal dawn, beyond a doubt,
> Shall break on hill and plain,
> And put all stars and candles out,
> Ere we be young again.

He never ceased to be young; he never lapsed from the child's philosophy:

The world is so full of a number of things,
I'm sure we should all be as happy as kings.

Genius never grows old: the child and the boy live on together in the heart of the man, the day dreamer. We think of Napoleon's day dream; to enter the golden East as a conqueror, riding a dromedary, and 'reading a Koran of my own composition.' In his 'Corsair' and 'Lara' the boy that was in Byron plays at being a pirate. 'Nobody knows what I was doing,' in a certain year, he writes in his Journal. His hope is that the Journal will be read, some day, by others, who will believe that he was a sea-rover, 'Byron the Red Handed,' like Huckleberry Finn. Stevenson, too, 'smells May and April' in his verse and prose, which are for ever green. *La mort n'y mord.*

A L.

CONTENTS

A CHILD'S GARDEN

CONTENTS xxi

THE CHILD ALONE

GARDEN DAYS

ENVOYS

A CHILD'S GARDEN

OF VERSES

BED IN SUMMER

IN winter I get up at night
    And dress by yellow candle-light.
In summer, quite the other way,
I have to go to bed by day.

I have to go to bed and see
The birds still hopping on the tree,
Or hear the grown-up people's feet
Still going past me in the street.

And does it not seem hard to you,
When all the sky is clear and blue,
And I should like so much to play,
To have to go to bed by day?

II.

A THOUGHT

I T is very nice to think
     The world is full of meat and drink,
With little children saying grace
In every Christian kind of place.

III

AT THE SEASIDE

WHEN I was down beside the sea
    A wooden spade they gave to me
  To dig the sandy shore.
My holes were empty like a cup,
In every hole the sea came up,
  Till it could come no more.

IV

YOUNG NIGHT THOUGHT

ALL night long and every night,
    When my mamma puts out the light,
I see the people marching by,
As plain as day, before my eye.

Armies and emperors and kings,
All carrying different kinds of things,
And marching in so grand a way,
You never saw the like by day.

So fine a show was never seen,
At the great circus on the green ;
For every kind of beast and man
Is marching in that caravan.

At first they move a little slow,
But still the faster on they go,
And still beside them close I keep
Until we reach the town of Sleep.

V

WHOLE DUTY OF CHILDREN

A CHILD should always say what 's true
 And speak when he is spoken to,
And behave mannerly at table :
At least as far as he is able.

VI

RAIN

THE rain is raining all around,
   It falls on field and tree,
It rains on the umbrellas here,
   And on the ships at sea.

VII

PIRATE STORY

THREE of us afloat in the meadow by
the swing,
Three of us aboard in the basket on the
lea.
Winds are in the air, they are blowing in
the spring,
And waves are on the meadow like the
waves there are at sea.

Where shall we adventure, to-day that we 're
    afloat,
  Wary of the weather and steering by a
    star ?
Shall it be to Africa, a-steering of the boat,
  To Providence, or Babylon, or off to
    Malabar ?

Hi ! but here 's a squadron a rowing on the
    sea—
  Cattle on the meadow a-charging with a
    roar !
Quick, and we 'll escape them, they 're as
    mad as they can be,
  The wicket is the harbour and the garden
    is the shore.

VIII

FOREIGN LANDS

UP into the cherry tree
    Who should climb but little me?
I held the trunk with both my hands
And looked abroad on foreign lands.

I saw the next door garden lie,
Adorned with flowers, before my eye,
And many pleasant places more
That I had never seen before.

I saw the dimpling river pass
And be the sky's blue looking-glass;
The dusty roads go up and down
With people tramping in to town.

If I could find a higher tree
Farther and farther I should see,
To where the grown-up river slips
Into the sea among the ships,

To where the roads on either hand
Lead onward into fairy land,
Where all the children dine at five,
And all the playthings come alive.

IX

WINDY NIGHTS

WHENEVER the moon and stars are
  set,
  Whenever the wind is high,
All night long in the dark and wet,
  A man goes riding by.
Late in the night when the fires are out,
Why does he gallop and gallop about?

Whenever the trees are crying aloud,
  And ships are tossed at sea,

By, on the highway, low and loud,
  By at the gallop goes he.
By at the gallop he goes, and then
By he comes back at the gallop again.

X

TRAVEL

I SHOULD like to rise and go
   Where the golden apples grow ;—
Where below another sky
Parrot islands anchored lie,
And, watched by cockatoos and goats,
Lonely Crusoes building boats ; —
Where in sunshine reaching out
Eastern cities, miles about,
Are with mosque and minaret
Among sandy gardens set,

C

And the rich goods from near and far
Hang for sale in the bazaar ;--
Where the Great Wall round China goes,
And on one side the desert blows,
And with bell and voice and drum,
Cities on the other hum ;—
Where are forests, hot as fire,
Wide as England, tall as a spire.
Full of apes and cocoa-nuts
And the negro hunters' huts ;--
Where the knotty crocodile
Lies and blinks in the Nile,
And the red flamingo flies
Hunting fish before his eyes ;—
Where in jungles, near and far,
Man-devouring tigers are,
Lying close and giving ear
Lest the hunt be drawing near,

Or a comer-by be seen
Swinging in a palanquin ;—
Where among the desert sands
Some deserted city stands,
All its children, sweep and prince,
Grown to manhood ages since,
Not a foot in street or house,
Not a stir of child or mouse,
And when kindly falls the night,
In all the town no spark of light.
There I 'll come when I 'm a man
With a camel caravan ;
Light a fire in the gloom
Of some dusty dining room ;
See the pictures on the walls,
Heroes, fights and festivals ;
And in a corner find the toys
Of the old Egyptian boys.

XI

SINGING

OF speckled eggs the birdie sings
   And nests among the trees;
The sailor sings of ropes and things
   In ships upon the seas.

The children sing in far Japan,
   The children sing in Spain;
The organ with the organ man
   Is singing in the rain.

XII

LOOKING FORWARD

WHEN I am grown to man's estate
    I shall be very proud and great,
And tell the other girls and boys
Not to meddle with my toys.

XIII

A GOOD PLAY

WE built a ship upon the stairs
    All made of the back-bedroom
      chairs,
And filled it full of sofa pillows
To go a-sailing on the billows.

We took a saw and several nails,
And water in the nursery pails;
And Tom said, 'Let us also take
An apple and a slice of cake;'—

Which was enough for Tom and me
To go a-sailing on, till tea.

We sailed along for days and days,
And had the very best of plays ;
But Tom fell out and hurt his knee,
So there was no one left but me.

XIV

WHERE GO THE BOATS?

DARK brown is the river,
　　Golden is the sand.
It flows along for ever,
　　With trees on either hand.

Green leaves a-floating,
　　Castles of the foam,
Boats of mine a-boating—
　　Where will all come home?

On goes the river
   And out past the mill,
Away down the valley,
   Away down the hill.

Away down the river,
   A hundred miles or more,
Other little children
   Shall bring my boats ashore.

XV

AUNTIE'S SKIRTS

WHENEVER Auntie moves around,
    Her dresses make a curious sound;
They trail behind her up the floor,
And trundle after through the door.

XVI

THE LAND OF COUNTERPANE

WHEN I was sick and lay a-bed,
    I had two pillows at my head,
And all my toys beside me lay
To keep me happy all the day.

And sometimes for an hour or so
I watched my leaden soldiers go,
With different uniforms and drills,
Among the bed-clothes, through the hills;

And sometimes sent my ships in fleets
All up and down among the sheets;
Or brought my trees and houses out,
And planted cities all about.

I was the giant great and still
That sits upon the pillow-hill,
And sees before him, dale and plain,
The pleasant land of counterpane.

XVII

THE LAND OF NOD

FROM breakfast on all through the day
    At home among my friends I stay ;
But every night I go abroad
Afar into the land of Nod.

All by myself I have to go,
With none to tell me what to do—
All alone beside the streams
And up the mountain-sides of dreams.

The strangest things are there for me,
Both things to eat and things to see,
And many frightening sights abroad
Till morning in the land of Nod.

Try as I like to find the way,
I never can get back by day,
Nor can remember plain and clear
The curious music that I hear.

XVIII

MY SHADOW

I HAVE a little shadow that goes in and
    out with me,
And what can be the use of him is more
    than I can see.
He is very, very like me from the heels up
    to the head ;
And I see him jump before me, when I
    jump into my bed.

The funniest thing about him is the way he
    likes to grow—
Not at all like proper children, which is
    always very slow;
For he sometimes shoots up taller like an
    india-rubber ball,
And he sometimes gets so little that there's
    none of him at all.

He hasn't got a notion of how children
    ought to play,
And can only make a fool of me in every
    sort of way.
He stays so close beside me, he's a coward
    you can see;
I'd think shame to stick to nursie as that
    shadow sticks to me!

One morning, very early, before the sun was
    up,
I rose and found the shining dew on every
    buttercup;
But my lazy little shadow, like an arrant
    sleepy-head,
Had stayed at home behind me and was fast
    asleep in bed.

XIX

SYSTEM

EVERY night my prayers I say,
    And get my dinner every day ;
And every day that I 've been good,
I get an orange after food.

The child that is not clean and neat,
With lots of toys and things to eat,
He is a naughty child, I'm sure—
Or else his dear papa is poor.

XX

A GOOD BOY

I WOKE before the morning, I was
 happy all the day,
I never said an ugly word, but smiled and
 stuck to play.

And now at last the sun is going down
 behind the wood,
And I am very happy, for I know that I 've
 been good.

My bed is waiting cool and fresh, with
   linen smooth and fair,
And I must off to sleepsin-by, and not
   forget my prayer.

I know that, till to.morrow I shall see the
   sun arise,
No ugly dream shall fright my mind, no
   ugly sight my eyes,

But slumber hold me tightly till I waken in
   the dawn,
And hear the thrushes singing in the lilacs
   round the lawn.

XXI

ESCAPE AT BEDTIME

THE lights from the parlour and kitchen
  shone out
  Through the blinds and the windows and
    bars ;
And high overhead and all moving about,
  There were thousands of millions of stars.
There ne'er were such thousands of leaves
    on a tree,
  Nor of people in church or the Park,

As the crowds of the stars that looked down
    upon me,
  And that glittered and winked in the
    dark.

The Dog, and the Plough, and the Hunter,
    and all,
  And the star of the sailor, and Mars,
These shone in the sky, and the pail by the
    wall
  Would be half full of water and stars.
They saw me at last, and they chased me
    with cries,
  And they soon had me packed into bed;
But the glory kept shining and bright in my
    eyes,
  And the stars going round in my head.

XXII

MARCHING SONG

BRING the comb and play upon it!
  Marching, here we come!
Willie cocks his highland bonnet,
  Johnnie beats the drum.

Mary Jane commands the party,
  Peter leads the rear;
Feet in time, alert and hearty,
  Each a Grenadier!

All in the most martial manner
  Marching double-quick;
While the napkin like a banner
  Waves upon the stick!

Here 's enough of fame and pillage,
  Great commander Jane!
Now that we 've been round the village,
  Let 's go home again.

XXIII

THE COW

THE friendly cow all red and white,
  I love with all my heart:
She gives me cream with all her might,
  To eat with apple-tart.

She wanders lowing here and there,
  And yet she cannot stray,
All in the pleasant open air,
  The pleasant light of day;

And blown by all the winds that pass
And wet with all the showers,
She walks among the meadow grass
And eats the meadow flowers.

XXIV

HAPPY THOUGHT

THE world is so full of a number of
things,
I 'm sure we should all be as happy as
kings.

XXV

THE WIND

I SAW you toss the kites on high
    And blow the birds about the sky;
And all around I heard you pass,
Like ladies' skirts across the grass—
    O wind, a-blowing all day long,
    O wind, that sings so loud a song!

I saw the different things you did,
But always you yourself you hid.

THE WIND

I felt you push, I heard you call,
I could not see yourself at all—
    O wind, a-blowing all day long,
    O wind, that sings so loud a song!

O you that are so strong and cold,
O blower, are you young or old?
Are you a beast of field and tree,
Or just a stronger child than me?
    O wind, a-blowing all day long,
    O wind, that sings so loud a song!

XXVI

KEEPSAKE MILL

OVER the borders, a sin without pardon,
  Breaking the branches and crawling
  below,
Out through the breach in the wall of the
  garden,
  Down by the banks of the river, we go.

Here is the mill with the humming of
  thunder,
  Here is the weir with the wonder of
  foam,

Here is the sluice with the race running
  under—
Marvellous places, though handy to home!

Sounds of the village grow stiller and
  stiller,
Stiller the note of the birds on the hill;
Dusty and dim are the eyes of the miller,
Deaf are his ears with the moil of the
  mill.

Years may go by, and the wheel in the
  river
Wheel as it wheels for us, children, to-day,
Wheel and keep roaring and foaming for
  ever
Long after all of the boys are away.

Home from the Indies and home from the
    ocean,
  Heroes and soldiers we all shall come
    home;
Still we shall find the old mill wheel in
    motion,
  Turning and churning that river to foam.

You with the bean that I gave when we
    quarrelled,
  I with your marble of Saturday last,
Honoured and old and all gaily apparelled,
  Here we shall meet and remember the
    past.

XXVII

GOOD AND BAD CHILDREN

CHILDREN, you are very little,
   And your bones are very brittle ;
If you would grow great and stately,
You must try to walk sedately.

You must still be bright and quiet,
And content with simple diet ;
And remain, through all bewild'ring,
Innocent and honest children.

E

Happy hearts and happy faces,
Happy play in grassy places—
That was how, in ancient ages,
Children grew to kings and sages.

But the unkind and the unruly,
And the sort who eat unduly,
They must never hope for glory—
Theirs is quite a different story!

Cruel children, crying babies,
All grow up as geese and gabies,
Hated, as their age increases,
By their nephews and their nieces.

XXVIII

FOREIGN CHILDREN

LITTLE Indian, Sioux or Crow,
  Little frosty Eskimo,
Little Turk or Japanee,
O! don't you wish that you were me?

You have seen the scarlet trees
And the lions over seas;
You have eaten ostrich eggs,
And turned the turtles off their legs.

Such a life is very fine,
But it 's not so nice as mine :
You must often, as you trod,
Have wearied *not* to be abroad.

You have curious things to eat,
I am fed on proper meat ;
You must dwell beyond the foam,
But I am safe and live at home.

Little Indian, Sioux or Crow,
Little frosty Eskimo,
Little Turk or Japanee,
O ! don't you wish that you were me ?

XXIX

THE SUN'S TRAVELS

THE sun is not a-bed, when I
    At night upon my pillow lie ;
Still round the earth his way he takes,
And morning after morning makes.

While here at home, in shining day,
We round the sunny garden play,
Each little Indian sleepy-head
Is being kissed and put to bed.

And when at eve I rise from tea,
Day dawns beyond the Atlantic Sea,
And all the children in the West
Are getting up and being dressed.

xxx

THE LAMPLIGHTER

MY tea is nearly ready and the sun has
    left the sky;
It 's time to take the window to see Leerie
    going by;
For every night at teatime and before you
    take your seat,
With lantern and with ladder he comes
    posting up the street.

Now Tom would be a driver and Maria go
    to sea,
And my papa 's a banker and as rich as he
    can be ;
But I, when I am stronger and can choose
    what I 'm to do,
O Leerie, I 'll go round at night and light
    the lamps with you !

For we are very lucky, with a lamp before
    the door,
And Leerie stops to light it as he lights so
    many more ;
And O ! before you hurry by with ladder and
    with light,
O Leerie, see a little child and nod to him
    to-night !

XXXI

MY BED IS A BOAT

MY bed is like a little boat;
    Nurse helps me in when I embark;
She girds me in my sailor's coat
    And starts me in the dark.

At night, I go on board and say
    Good night to all my friends on shore;
I shut my eyes and sail away
    And see and hear no more.

And sometimes things to bed I take,
  As prudent sailors have to do :
Perhaps a slice of wedding-cake,
  Perhaps a toy or two.

All night across the dark we steer :
  But when the day returns at last
Safe in my room, beside the pier,
  I find my vessel fast.

XXXII

THE MOON

THE moon has a face like the clock in
    the hall;
She shines on thieves on the garden wall,
On streets and fields and harbour quays,
And birdies asleep in the forks of the trees.

The squalling cat and the squeaking mouse,
The howling dog by the door of the house,
The bat that lies in bed at noon,
All love to be out by the light of the moon.

But all of the things that belong to the day
Cuddle to sleep to be out of her way;
And flowers and children close their eyes
Till up in the morning the sun shall arise.

XXXIII

THE SWING

HOW do you like to go up in a swing,
    Up in the air so blue?
Oh, I do think it the pleasantest thing
    Ever a child can do!

Up in the air and over the wall,
    Till I can see so wide,
Rivers and trees and cattle and all
    Over the countryside—

Till I look down on the garden green,
 Down on the roof so brown—
Up in the air I go flying again,
 Up in the air and down!

XXXIV

TIME TO RISE

A BIRDIE with a yellow bill
    Hopped upon the window sill.
Cocked his shining eye and said:
'Ain't you 'shamed, you sleepy-head?'

XXXV

LOOKING-GLASS RIVER

SMOOTH it slides upon its travel,
  Here a wimple, there a gleam—
    O the clean gravel!
    O the smooth stream!

Sailing blossoms, silver fishes,
  Paven pools as clear as air—
    How a child wishes
    To live down there!

We can see our coloured faces
  Floating on the shaken pool
    Down in cool places,
    Dim and very cool;

Till a wind or water wrinkle,
  Dipping marten, plumping trout,
    Spreads in a twinkle
    And blots all out.

See the rings pursue each other;
  All below grows black as night,
    Just as if mother
    Had blown out the light!

F

Patience, children, just a minute—
See the spreading circles die;
The stream and all in it
Will clear by-and-by.

XXXVI

FAIRY BREAD

COME up here, O dusty feet!
    Here is fairy bread to eat
Here in my retiring room,
    Children, you may dine
On the golden smell of broom
    And the shade of pine;
And when you have eaten well,
Fairy stories hear and tell.

XXXVII

FROM A RAILWAY CARRIAGE

FASTER than fairies, faster than witches,
    Bridges and houses, hedges and
  ditches ;
And charging along like troops in a battle,
All through the meadows the horses and
  cattle :
All of the sights of the hill and the plain
Fly as thick as driving rain ;
And ever again, in the wink of an eye,
Painted stations whistle by.

Here is a child who clambers and scrambles,

All by himself and gathering brambles;

Here is a tramp who stands and gazes;

And there is the green for stringing the
daisies!

Here is a cart run away in the road

Lumping along with man and load;

And here is a mill and there is a river:

Each a glimpse and gone for ever!

XXXVIII

WINTER-TIME

LATE lies the wintry sun a-bed,
  A frosty, fiery sleepy-head ;
Blinks but an hour or two ; and then,
A blood-red orange, sets again.

Before the stars have left the skies,
At morning in the dark I rise ;
And shivering in my nakedness,
By the cold candle, bathe and dress.

Close by the jolly fire I sit
To warm my frozen bones a bit;
Or with a reindeer sled, explore
The colder countries round the door.

When to go out, my nurse doth wrap
Me in my comforter and cap:
The cold wind burns my face, and blows
Its frosty pepper up my nose.

Black are my steps on silver sod;
Thick blows my frosty breath abroad;
And tree and house, and hill and lake,
Are frosted like a wedding-cake.

XXXIX

THE HAYLOFT

THROUGH all the pleasant meadow-side
  The grass grew shoulder-high,
Till the shining scythes went far and wide
  And cut it down to dry.

These green and sweetly smelling crops
  They led in waggons home;
And they piled them here in mountain tops
  For mountaineers to roam.

Here is Mount Clear, Mount Rusty-Nail,
  Mount Eagle and Mount High ;—
The mice that in these mountains dwell,
  No happier are than I !

O what a joy to clamber there,
  O what a place for play,
With the sweet, the dim, the dusty air,
  The happy hills of hay.

XL

FAREWELL TO THE FARM

THE coach is at the door at last;
    The eager children, mounting fast
And kissing hands, in chorus sing:
Good-bye, good-bye, to everything!

To house and garden, field and lawn,
The meadow-gates we swang upon,
To pump and stable, tree and swing,
Good-bye, good-bye, to everything!

And fare you well for evermore,
O ladder at the hayloft door,
O hayloft where the cobwebs cling,
Good-bye, good-bye, to everything !

Crack goes the whip, and off we go ;
The trees and houses smaller grow ;
Last, round the woody turn we swing :
Good-bye, good-bye, to everything !

XLI

NORTH-WEST PASSAGE

1. Good Night.

WHEN the bright lamp is carried in,
⠀⠀⠀The sunless hours again begin ;
O'er all without, in field and lane,
The haunted night returns again.

Now we behold the embers flee
About the firelit hearth ; and see
Our faces painted as we pass,
Like pictures, on the window-glass.

Must we to bed indeed? Well then,
Let us arise and go like men,
And face with an undaunted tread
The long black passage up to bed.

Farewell, O brother, sister, sire!
O pleasant party round the fire!
The songs you sing, the tales you tell,
Till far to-morrow, fare ye weil!

2. Shadow March.

All round the house is the jet-black night;
  It stares through the window-pane;
It crawls in the corners, hiding from the
    light,
  And it moves with the moving flame.

Now my little heart goes a-beating like a
    drum,
  With the breath of the Bogie in my hair;
And all round the candle the crooked shadows
    come
  And go marching along up the stair.

The shadow of the balusters, the shadow of
the lamp,

The shadow of the child that goes to
bed—

All the wicked shadows coming, tramp, tramp,
tramp,

With the black night overhead.

3. IN PORT.

Last, to the chamber where I lie
My fearful footsteps patter nigh,
And come from out the cold and gloom
Into my warm and cheerful room.

There, safe arrived, we turn about
To keep the coming shadows out,
And close the happy door at last
On all the perils that we past.

Then, when mamma goes by to bed,
She shall come in with tip-toe tread,
And see me lying warm and fast
And in the Land of Nod at last.

THE CHILD ALONE

1

THE UNSEEN PLAYMATE

WHEN children are playing alone on the
green,
In comes the playmate that never was seen.
When children are happy and lonely and
good,
The Friend of the Children comes out of the
wood.

Nobody heard him and nobody saw,
His is a picture you never could draw,

But he 's sure to be present, abroad or at
    home,
When children are happy and playing alone.

He lies in the laurels, he runs on the grass,
He sings when you tinkle the musical glass ;
Whene'er you are happy and cannot tell
    why,
The Friend of the Children is sure to be by !

He loves to be little, he hates to be big,
'T is he that inhabits the caves that you
    dig ;
'T is he when you play with your soldiers of
    tin
That sides with the Frenchmen and never can
    win.

'T is he, when at night you go off to your
    bed,

Bids you go to your sleep and not trouble
    your head ;

For wherever they 're lying, in cupboard or
    shelf,

'T is he will take care of your playthings
    himself !

II

MY SHIP AND I

O IT 'S I that am the captain of a tidy
  little ship,
  Of a ship that goes a-sailing on the
    pond ;
And my ship it keeps a-turning all around
    and all about ;

But when I 'm a little older, I shall find the
     secret out
  How to send my vessel sailing on beyond.

For I mean to grow as little as the dolly at
     the helm,
  And the dolly I intend to come alive;
And with him beside to help me, it 's a-sailing
     I shall go,
It 's a-sailing on the water, when the jolly
     breezes blow
  And the vessel goes a divie-divie dive.

O it 's then you 'll see me sailing through
     the rushes and the reeds,
  And you 'll hear the water singing at the
     prow;

For beside the dolly sailor, I 'm to voyage and
    explore,
To land upon the island where no dolly was
    before,
    And to fire the penny cannon in the bow.

III

MY KINGDOM

DOWN by a shining water well
 I found a very little dell,
No higher than my head.
The heather and the gorse about
In summer bloom were coming out,
 Some yellow and some red.

I called the little pool a sea;
The little hills were big to me;
 For I am very small.

I made a boat, I made a town,
I searched the caverns up and down,
    And named them one and all.

And all about was mine, I said,
The little sparrows overhead,
    The little minnows too.
This was the world and I was king;
For me the bees came by to sing,
    For me the swallows flew.

I played there were no deeper seas,
Nor any wider plains than these,
    Nor other kings than me.
At last I heard my mother call
Out from the house at evenfall,
    To call me home to tea.

And I must rise and leave my dell,

And leave my dimpled water well,

And leave my heather blooms.

Alas! and as my home I neared,

How very big my nurse appeared,

How great and cool the rooms!

IV

PICTURE-BOOKS IN WINTER

SUMMER fading, winter comes—
  Frosty mornings, tingling thumbs,
Window robins, winter rooks,
And the picture story-books.

Water now is turned to stone
Nurse and I can walk upon;
Still we find the flowing brooks
In the picture story-books.

All the pretty things put by,
Wait upon the children's eye,
Sheep and shepherds, trees and crooks,
In the picture story-books.

We may see how all things are,
Seas and cities, near and far,
And the flying fairies' looks,
In the picture story-books.

How am I to sing your praise,
Happy chimney-corner days,
Sitting safe in nursery nooks,
Reading picture story-books?

V

MY TREASURES

THESE nuts, that I keep in the back of
the nest
Where all my lead soldiers are lying at
rest,
Were gathered in autumn by nursie and me
In a wood with a well by the side of the
sea.

This whistle we made (and how clearly it
 sounds !)
By the side of a field at the end of the
 grounds.
Of a branch of a plane, with a knife of my
 own,
It was nursie who made it, and nursie
 alone !

The stone, with the white and the yellow
 and grey,
We discovered I cannot tell *how* far away ;
And I carried it back although weary and
 cold,
For though father denies it, I 'm sure it is
 gold.

H

But of all of my treasures the last is the
    king,
For there 's very few children possess such
    a thing ;
And that is a chisel, both handle and blade,
Which a man who was really a carpenter
    made.

VI

BLOCK CITY

WHAT are you able to build with your
    blocks?
Castles and palaces, temples and docks.
Rain may keep raining, and others go roam,
But I can be happy and building at home.

Let the sofa be mountains, the carpet be
    sea,
There I 'll establish a city for me:

A kirk and a mill and a palace beside,
And a harbour as well where my vessels
    may ride.

Great is the palace with pillar and wall,
A sort of a tower on the top of it all,
And steps coming down in an orderly way
To where my toy vessels lie safe in the
    bay.

This one is sailing and that one is moored :
Hark to the song of the sailors on board !
And see on the steps of my palace, the
    kings
Coming and going with presents and
    things !

Now I have done with it, down let it go!
All in a moment the town is laid low.
Block upon block lying scattered and free,
What is there left of my town by the sea?

Yet as I saw it, I see it again,
The kirk and the palace. the ships and the
   men,
And as long as I live and where'er I may
   be,
I 'll always remember my town by the sea.

VII

THE LAND OF STORY-BOOKS

AT evening when the lamp is lit,
    Around the fire my parents sit;
They sit at home and talk and sing,
And do not play at anything.

Now, with my little gun, I crawl
All in the dark along the wall,
And follow round the forest track
Away behind the sofa back.

There, in the night, where none can spy,
All in my hunter's camp I lie,
And play at books that I have read
Till it is time to go to bed.

These are the hills, these are the woods,
These are my starry solitudes ;
And there the river by whose brink
The roaring lions come to drink.

I see the others far away
As if in firelit camp they lay,
And I, like to an Indian scout,
Around their party prowled about.

So, when my nurse comes in for me,
Home I return across the sea,
And go to bed with backward looks
At my dear land of Story-books.

VIII

ARMIES IN THE FIRE

THE lamps now glitter down the street;
Faintly sound the falling feet;
And the blue even slowly falls
About the garden trees and walls.

Now in the falling of the gloom
The red fire paints the empty room:
And warmly on the roof it looks,
And flickers on the backs of books.

Armies march by tower and spire
Of cities blazing, in the fire ;—
Till as I gaze with staring eyes,
The armies fade, the lustre dies.

Then once again the glow returns;
Again the phantom city burns ;
And down the red-hot valley, lo !
The phantom armies marching go !

Blinking embers, tell me true
Where are those armies marching to,
And what the burning city is
That crumbles in your furnaces !

IX

THE LITTLE LAND

WHEN at home alone I sit
    And am very tired of it,
I have just to shut my eyes
To go sailing through the skies—
To go sailing far away
To the pleasant Land of Play;
To the fairy land afar
Where the Little People are;
Where the clover-tops are trees,
And the rain-pools are the seas,

And the leaves like little ships
Sail about on tiny trips ;
And above the daisy tree
   Through the grasses,
High o'erhead the Bumble Bee
   Hums and passes.

In that forest to and fro
I can wander, I can go ;
See the spider and the fly,
And the ants go marching by
Carrying parcels with their feet
Down the green and grassy street.
I can in the sorrel sit
Where the ladybird alit.
I can climb the jointed grass ;
   And on high

See the greater swallows pass
In the sky,
And the round sun rolling by
Heeding no such things as I.

Through that forest I can pass
Till, as in a looking-glass,
Humming fly and daisy tree
And my tiny self I see,
Painted very clear and neat
On the rain-pool at my feet.
Should a leaflet come to land
Drifting near to where I stand,
Straight I 'll board that tiny boat
Round the rain-pool sea to float.

Little thoughtful creatures sit
On the grassy coasts of it ;

Little things with lovely eyes
See me sailing with surprise.
Some are clad in armour green—
(These have sure to battle been!)—
Some are pied with ev'ry hue,
Black and crimson, gold and blue ;
Some have wings and swift are gone ;—
But they all look kindly on.

When my eyes I once again
Open, and see all things plain :
High bare walls, great bare floor ;
Great big knobs on drawer and door ;
Great big people perched on chairs,
Stitching tucks and mending tears,
Each a hill that I could climb,
And talking nonsense all the time—

O dear me,
That I could be
A sailor on the rain-pool sea,
A climber in the clover tree,
And just come back, a sleepy-head,
Late at night to go to bed.

GARDEN DAYS

1

NIGHT AND DAY

WHEN the golden day is done,
   Through the closing portal,
Child and garden, flower and sun,
   Vanish all things mortal.

As the blinding shadows fall,
   As the rays diminish,
Under evening's cloak, they all
   Roll away and vanish.

Garden darkened, daisy shut,
  Child in bed, they slumber—
Glow-worm in the highway rut,
  Mice among the lumber.

In the darkness houses shine,
  Parents move with candles;
Till on all, the night divine
  Turns the bedroom handles.

Till at last the day begins
  In the east a-breaking,
In the hedges and the whins
  Sleeping birds a-waking.

In the darkness shapes of things,
  Houses, trees, and hedges,
Clearer grow; and sparrow's wings
  Beat on window ledges.

These shall wake the yawning maid;
  She the door shall open—
Finding dew on garden glade
  And the morning broken.

There my garden grows again
  Green and rosy painted,
As at eve behind the pane
  From my eyes it fainted.

Just as it was shut away,
  Toy-like, in the even,
Here I see it glow with day
  Under glowing heaven.

Every path and every plot,
  Every bush of roses,
Every blue forget-me-not
  Where the dew reposes,

' Up !' they cry, 'the day is come
On the smiling valleys ;
We have beat the morning drum ;
Playmate, join your allies !'

II

NEST EGGS

Birds all the sunny day
   Flutter and quarrel
Here in the arbour-like
  Tent of the laurel.

Here in the fork
  The brown nest is seated;
Four little blue eggs
  The mother keeps heated.

While we stand watching her,
    Staring like gabies,
Safe in each egg are the
    Bird's little babies.

Soon the frail eggs they shall
    Chip, and upspringing
Make all the April woods
    Merry with singing.

Younger than we are,
    O children, and frailer,
Soon in blue air they 'll be,
    Singer and sailor.

We, so much older,
    Taller and stronger,
We shall look down on the
    Birdies no longer.

They shall go flying
  With musical speeches
High overhead in the
  Tops of the beeches.

In spite of our wisdom
  And sensible talking,
We on our feet must go
  Plodding and walking.

III

THE FLOWERS

ALL the names I know from nurse:
  Gardener's garters, Shepherd's purse,
Bachelor's buttons, Lady's smock,
And the Lady Hollyhock.

Fairy places, fairy things,
Fairy woods where the wild bee wings,
Tiny trees for tiny dames—
These must all be fairy names!

Tiny woods below whose boughs
Shady fairies weave a house ;
Tiny tree-tops, rose or thyme,
Where the braver fairies climb !

Fair are grown-up people's trees,
But the fairest woods are these ;
Where if I were not so tall,
I should live for good and all.

IV

SUMMER SUN

G REAT is the sun, and wide he goes
   Through   empty   heaven   without
   repose ;
And in the blue and glowing days
More thick than rain he showers his rays.

Though closer still the blinds we pull
To keep the shady parlour cool,
Yet he will find a chink or two
To slip his golden fingers through.

The dusty attic spider-clad
He, through the keyhole, maketh glad ;
And through the broken edge of tiles,
Into the laddered hayloft smiles.

Meantime his golden face around
He bares to all the garden ground,
And sheds a warm and glittering look
Among the ivy's inmost nook.

Above the hills, along the blue,
Round the bright air with footing true,
To please the child, to paint the rose,
The gardener of the World, he goes.

V

THE DUMB SOLDIER

WHEN the grass was closely mown,
    Walking on the lawn alone,
In the turf a hole I found
And hid a soldier underground

Spring and daisies came apace ;
Grasses hide my hiding place ;
Grasses run like a green sea
O'er the lawn up to my knee.

Under grass alone he lies,
Looking up with leaden eyes,
Scarlet coat and pointed gun,
To the stars and to the sun.

When the grass is ripe like grain,
When the scythe is stoned again,
When the lawn is shaven clear,
Then my hole shall reappear.

I shall find him, never fear,
I shall find my grenadier;
But for all that 's gone and come,
I shall find my soldier dumb.

He has lived, a little thing,
In the grassy woods of spring;
Done, if he could tell me true,
Just as I should like to do

He has seen the starry hours
And the springing of the flowers;
And the fairy things that pass
In the forests of the grass.

In the silence he has heard
Talking bee and ladybird,
And the butterfly has flown
O'er him as he lay alone.

Not a word will he disclose,
Not a word of all he knows.
I must lay him on the shelf,
And make up the tale myself.

K

VI

AUTUMN FIRES

IN the other gardens
   And all up the vale,
From the autumn bonfires
   See the smoke trail!

Pleasant summer over
   And all the summer flowers,
The red fire blazes,
   The grey smoke towers.

Sing a song of seasons !
  Something bright in all !
Flowers in the summer,
  Fires in the fall !

VII

THE GARDENER

THE gardener does not love to talk,
　　He makes me keep the gravel walk ;
And when he puts his tools away,
He locks the door and takes the key.

Away behind the currant row
Where no one else but cook may go,
Far in the plots, I see him dig,
Old and serious, brown and big.

He digs the flowers, green, red, and blue,
Nor wishes to be spoken to.
He digs the flowers and cuts the hay,
And never seems to want to play.

Silly gardener! summer goes,
And winter comes with pinching toes,
When in the garden bare and brown
You must lay your barrow down.

Well now, and while the summer stays,
To profit by these garden days,
O how much wiser you would be
To play at Indian wars with me!

VIII

HISTORICAL ASSOCIATIONS

DEAR Uncle Jim, this garden ground
    That now you smoke your pipe
        around,
Has seen immortal actions done
And valiant battles lost and won.

Here we had best on tip-toe tread,
While I for safety march ahead,
For this is that enchanted ground
Where all who loiter slumber sound.

Here is the sea, here is the sand,
Here is simple Shepherd's Land,
Here are the fairy hollyhocks,
And there are Ali Baba's rocks.

But yonder, see! apart and high,
Frozen Siberia lies; where I,
With Robert Bruce and William Tell,
Was bound by an enchanter's spell.

There, then, awhile in chains we lay,
In wintry dungeons, far from day;
But ris'n at length, with might and main,
Our iron fetters burst in twain.

Then all the horns were blown in town;
And to the ramparts clanging down,
All the giants leaped to horse
And charged behind us through the gorse.

On we rode, the others and I,
Over the mountains blue, and by
The Silver River, the sounding sea,
And the robber woods of Tartary.

A thousand miles we galloped fast,
And down the witches' lane we passed,
And rode amain, with brandished sword,
Up to the middle, through the ford.

Last we drew rein—a weary three—
Upon the lawn, in time for tea,
And from our steeds alighted down
Before the gates of Babylon.

ENVOYS

I

TO WILLIE AND HENRIETTA

IF two may read aright
  These rhymes of old delight
And house and garden play,
You two, my cousins, and you only, may.

You in a garden green
With me were king and queen,
Were hunter, soldier, tar,
And all the thousand things that children
    are.

Now in the elders' seat
We rest with quiet feet,
And from the window-bay
We watch the children, our successors, play.

'Time was,' the golden head
Irrevocably said ;
But time which none can bind,
While flowing fast away, leaves love behind.

II

TO MY MOTHER

YOU too, my mother, read my rhymes
    For love of unforgotten times,
And you may chance to hear once more
The little feet along the floor.

III

TO AUNTIE

CHIEF *of our aunts—not only* I,
    But all your dozen of nurslings cry—
What did the other children do?
And what were childhood, wanting you?

IV

TO MINNIE

THE red room with the giant bed
    Where none but elders laid their
      head ;
The little room where you and I
Did for awhile together lie
And, simple suitor, I your hand
In decent marriage did demand ;
The great day nursery, best of all,
With pictures pasted on the wall

And leaves upon the blind—
A pleasant room wherein to wake
And hear the leafy garden shake
And rustle in the wind—
And pleasant there to lie in bed
And see the pictures overhead—
The wars about Sebastopol,
The grinning guns along the wall,
The daring escalade,
The plunging ships, the bleating sheep,
The happy children ankle-deep
And laughing as they wade:
All these are vanished clean away,
And the old manse is changed to-day;
It wears an altered face
And shields a stranger race.
The river, on from mill to mill,
Flows past our childhood's garden still;

But ah! we children never more
Shall watch it from the water-door!
Below the yew—it still is there—
Our phantom voices haunt the air
As we were still at play,
And I can hear them call and say:
'*How far is it to Babylon?*'

Ah, far enough, my dear,
Far, far enough from here—
Yet you have farther gone!
'*Can I get there by candlelight?*'
So goes the old refrain.
I do not know—perchance you might—
But only, children, hear it right,
Ah, never to return again!
The eternal dawn, beyond a doubt,
Shall break on hill and plain,

And put all stars and candles out,
Ere we be young again.

To you in distant India, these
I send across the seas,
Nor count it far across.
For which of us forgets
The Indian cabinets,
The bones of antelope, the wings of alba-
    tross,
The pied and painted birds and beans,
The junks and bangles, beads and screens,
The gods and sacred bells,
And the loud-humming, twisted shells?
The level of the parlour floor
Was honest, homely, Scottish shore ;
But when we climbed upon a chair,
Behold the gorgeous East was there !

Be this a fable ; and behold
Me in the parlour as of old,
And Minnie just above me set
In the quaint Indian cabinet !
Smiling and kind, you grace a shelf
Too high for me to reach myself.
Reach down a hand, my dear, and take
These rhymes for old acquaintance' sake.

V

TO MY NAME-CHILD

I

SOME day soon this rhyming volume, if
    you learn with proper speed,
Little Louis Sanchez, will be given you to
    read.
Then shall you discover, that your name was
    printed down
By the English printers, long before, in
    London town.

In the great and busy city where the East
   and West are met,
All the little letters did the English printer
   set ;
While you thought of nothing, and were still
   too young to play,
Foreign people thought of you in places far
   away.

Ay, and while you slept, a baby, over all the
   English lands
Other little children took the volume in their
   hands ;
Other children questioned, in their homes
   across the seas :
Who was little Louis, won't you tell us,
   mother, please ?

2

Now that you have spelt your lesson, lay it
    down and go and play,
Seeking shells and seaweed on the sands of
    Monterey,
Watching all the mighty whalebones, lying
    buried by the breeze,
Tiny sandy-pipers, and the huge Pacific seas.

And remember in your playing, as the sea-
    fog rolls to you,
Long ere you could read it, how I told you
    what to do ;

And that while you thought of no one, nearly
    half the world away
Some one thought of Louis on the beach of
    Monterey !

VI

TO ANY READER

As from the house your mother sees
    You playing round the garden trees,
So you may see, if you will look
Through the windows of this book,
Another child, far, far away,
And in another garden, play.
But do not think you can at all,
By knocking on the window, call
That child to hear you. He intent
Is all on his play-business bent.

He does not hear; he will not look,
Nor yet be lured out of this book.
For, long ago, the truth to say,
He has grown up and gone away,
And it is but a child of air
That lingers in the garden there.

PRINTED IN GREAT BRITAIN BY
WILLIAM CLOWES AND SONS, LIMITED,
BECCLES.